Ziyoda Quvvatova

New Page

AF168203

Ziyoda Quvvatova

New Page

This anthology is a collection of works of young authors

JustFiction Edition

Imprint

Any brand names and product names mentioned in this book are subject to trademark, brand or patent protection and are trademarks or registered trademarks of their respective holders. The use of brand names, product names, common names, trade names, product descriptions etc. even without a particular marking in this work is in no way to be construed to mean that such names may be regarded as unrestricted in respect of trademark and brand protection legislation and could thus be used by anyone.

Cover image: www.ingimage.com

Publisher:
JustFiction! Edition
is a trademark of
Dodo Books Indian Ocean Ltd. and OmniScriptum S.R.L publishing group

120 High Road, East Finchley, London, N2 9ED, United Kingdom
Str. Armeneasca 28/1, office 1, Chisinau MD-2012, Republic of Moldova, Europe
Printed at: see last page
ISBN: 978-620-0-10617-9

Saydullayeva Marjonakhon

4th grade student of the 5th comprehensive school of Namangan city Saydullayeva Marjonakhon.

The day I was born, my father was more than happy. Because I am the only daughter in our family. My mother taught me that one should not be afraid to dream big from the moment one knows his mind. May 3 is my favorite day. As you know, I was born on this date. This day is widely celebrated as world press freedom day. Perhaps that is why I have a strong desire to become a journalist, poet, and creator. I want to be a doctor to help many people. But as my father always emphasized, being needed is the most important thing in life. When I achieve my wishes, when people see my success and say "Thank you Father", this is the greatest happiness for me.

FATHER

So that I can gain knowledge,

I must see it.

Thinking of me,

Everyone gave me a book, my father.

Read because you are a clever girl,

Because you will be left behind,

Because you are gentle and kind,

My father gave me a book.

My grandmother

When I see light from their faces,

When I ask them to speak wisdom.

I say that I am a very happy girl.

When I hold her hands tightly,

My prayers are amazingly beautiful grandmother,

The angel of our house is the light of my world.

Hamidullayeva Ziynatkhon

Hamidullayeva Ziynatkhon was born in 2009 in the village of Gova, Chust district, Namangan region. She is currently a 7th grade student of the 67th general secondary school. He has been passionate about poetry since childhood. Until now, my poetry collections "My dreams open flowers", "Motherland anthem in my heart" and "Suyuklisan tilginam" have been published. His poems have been published in various books and collections, newspapers and magazines. He is the winner of the national laureate of the Children's Art Festival "Rainbow Stars" held in 2022. He participates in district and regional cultural evenings.

MY MOTHER TONGUE

You are the most precious beloved for me, my dear,

My bright heart will be happy with you.

You are so kind and quiet like my mother,

You live in my body like an inseparable body.

My mother tongue never leave me

Do not take your heart from my heart,

You are always with me every second.

After all, all your love flows in my blood

You are the one who introduced me to my mother tongue,

You are the one who introduced me to my mother tongue.

I was looking for knowledge and learned from you,

Even if I forget for a moment, my tongue will not adjust.

MY FLAG

The high sky is constantly swaying,

Do not bend and do not break.

The symbol of achievements is the flag of Uzbekistan,

We have a higher human dignity.

The red colors in it are our blood in the veins,

White color is a symbol of peace, our living soul.

A green leaf is a reflection of the beauty around us,

Blue color is our peace and sky.

They are waving in the heights saying, "Long live my country."

Our anthem is resounding with joy to the hearts.

Our Tanhodir flag is the honor of our country,

Look at the beautiful nature on all four sides.

Brave and brave men who carry our flag,

There are strange people in the heavenly land.

Always stand up, my proud flag,

May my country be blessed, happy thirty-one years.

A WEAK MOTHER

If I get sick, he wakes up and dies,

How many complicated problems.

You have solved with your kindness,

He always opened his heart to me,

Munis, my mother, my mushtipar mother.

If I fall, I have a stick to lean on,

My happy face is like the moon.

He was killed by the stones thrown at him,

Munis, my mother, my mushtipar mother.

When luck turned away, he turned away,

He ran without looking back.

He cried out to God with open hands,

Munis, my mother, my mushtipar mother.

His hair is gray from various worries,

My mother likes what words and phrases.

From burning grief and worry,

Munis, my mother, my mushtipar mother.

Sherova Orzigul

Sherova Orzigul is a 3rd year student of Uzbekistan State University

Of World Languages. She was born in Khorezm region in 2000.

She graduated from school and college with honors. Author of many

Poems and art articles. Winner of many poetry contests. Many of

Her poems have been published in newspapers, magazines and books.

I WISH I HAD A HOUSE IN MADINA

The palace of the rich man, if not,

I am satisfied when I enter it.

I don't need it, my beauty,

I wish I had a house in Medina.

I don't need gold dice,

The feeling of heedlessness fades from the heart.

Do not wear silk, satin,

I wish I had a house in Medina.

Let the hearts be gentle,

All evil will die.

Hard, nice case,

I wish I had a house in Medina.

SICK HEART

An indelible place found in the web of the heart,

During the day, the sun accompanies the moon at night,

My feelings are flowing like a stream,

No, no, don't leave, you leave

My sick tongue is just angry.

My heart is half without you

I know that I can't wake up at night,

Call me my flower, my lonely angel,

No, no, don't leave, you leave

My sick tongue is just angry.

We made promises, sky,

Or do you doubt my love?

Questions still bother me

No, no, don't leave, you leave

My sick tongue is just angry.

   * * *

Go ahead and follow me,

Throw stones and smile.

After all, I'm still dry,

Check out the tracks I've covered.

Don't say it's a miracle, at least, woman.

What are you doing behind my back?

Maybe you won't find perfection,

Check out the tracks I've covered.

Taste the pains or pain,

You will also feel the pain from the tests,

Well, take a pen in your hand,

Check out the tracks I've covered.

Call me bad, call me weak, but not to me

The world does not know that I can endure

You and I will not be lucky or happy,

Check out the tracks I've covered.

Khoshimova Shahinabonu

Khoshimova Shahinabonu was born on August 23, 2007 in Mingbulok district of Namangan region.Currently, she's a student of school number 13 in Mingbulok district. She interested in writing articles and write articles often. She also write short instructive stories. Today, she a member of 2 international organizations.

ZAHIRIDDIN MUHAMMAD BABUR

Annotations: This article describes the life path and scientific heritage of Zahiriddin Muhammad Babur, as well as his significance today.

Key words: Great Babur Dynasty, "Boburnoma", Babur Park.

Zahiriddin Muhammad Babur, one of the great figures of Uzbek literature, literary scholar, great statesman, general, founder of the "Great Babur dynasty", was born on February 14, 1483 in the city of Andijan, in the family of Umarsheikh Mirzo, governor of the Fargona ulus, and Princess Qutlug Nigor Khanim, who was originally from Genghis. Will come.

Babur's father, Umarshaikh Mirza, was the governor of Fargona region, the vassal of Timurid Sultan Mironshah, and the 3rd son of Amir Temur. Babur's mother Qutlug Nigor Khanim was the daughter of Yunus Khan, one of the Mughal Khans.

Zahiruddin Muhammad Babur was nicknamed "Babur" because he was brave and fearless. The word "Babur" comes from the Persian language "babr", which means "leopard", "lion".

Like all princes, Zahiruddin Muhammad Babur was educated in his father's palace. However, Babur's father died in 1494 due to an accident. At that time, Central Asia was turbulent, wars for the throne were raging. Therefore, Babur was forced to ascend the throne at the age of 12. In the early years of his rule, a fierce struggle for the throne broke out among the Timurid princes. Young Zahiriddin has to fight for the throne of Andijan with his uncle Sultan Ahmad Mirza and his brother Jahangir Mirza. Babur tries to come to a compromise with his brother and gives Jahangir Mirza half of his Fargona ulus. And Ozi will enter the battles for Samarkand.

Struggles do not yield any results. And Babur fought several battles for India in 1519-1525 in order to restore his position. 1526 Battle of Panipat against Indian Sultan Ibrahim Lodi. In 1527, he fought with the governor of Chitora, Rano Sango. In both fights, Babur's hand comes out on top. In this way, Babur established a small power in India. The dynasty founded by Babur is one of the largest dynasties in history, and this dynasty ruled for 332 years, i.e. from 1526 to 1858.

India prospered during Babur's rule. Literature, art, urban planning will develop. A perfect spiritual and spiritual environment is created in the country. The great

Indian scholar Jawaharlal Nehru says about Babur: "After Babur's arrival in India, great changes took place and new incentives breathed fresh air into life, art, architecture, and other fields of culture became intertwined."

Babur's passion for Sharia never waned. The total size of Babur's lions will increase from 400. Among them, he created 119 ghazals, 231 rubai and tuyuq, qita, fard, and masnavi works.

Babur's masterpiece is "Baburnoma", which is also called "Waqoe". The great memorial work describes the events that took place in the years 1494-1529 in Central and Asia Minor, in the countries of the Near and Middle East. There are more than ten manuscript copies of "Boburnoma". Babur also wrote a scientific-theoretical work entitled "About Aruz" dedicated to the rules of writing poems in Uzbek languages. In addition, Babur tried to adapt and simplify the Arabic letters and the Turkish language and created a new alphabet – "Hatti Baburiy" (Babut letter).

Babur died in Agra in 1530 at the age of 47. Babur's tomb is located in the city of Kabul. There is a 40-hectare "Babur Garden" there, and the grave is located in this garden.

In 1993, the Babur National Park was established in Andijan city, 8 km from the center, in the south-east of Andijan, on the occasion of the 510th anniversary of the birth of the son of Andijan, king and poet Zahiriddin Muhammad Babur. The area of the park is 357 hectares.

Babur National Park is a place of recreation and pilgrimage. A statue of Babur is installed on the first platform. The "Babur and World Culture" museum stands above. The museum exhibits unique manuscripts, books and historical items brought by the international scientific expedition dedicated to the study of Babur's life and heritage, handwritten copies of Babur's works, especially Babur's own hand in "Hatti Baburi". Copies of the Holy Qur'an, weapons of the Babur period, clothes of courtiers, and coins minted by the Babur kings. Among the exhibits of the collection are literary works written by Babur and his children, especially his daughter Gulbadan-Begim, who inherited her father's poetic talent.

Currently, more than 200 thousand samples of Indian and foreign art are stored in the museum.

Currently, the museum is making a great contribution to the organization of our young people's history.

References

1. U. Erskin. The state of Babur in India (translated from English by G. Sotimov)-T.: 1997

2. R. Sharma. Babur kingdom (from English

G. Sotimov trans.)-T.: 1999

   3. Myself. The first volume-T.: 2000

4. V. Zohidov. About Babur's activity and scientific-literary heritage-T.:1960.

Quvvatova Ziyoda

Quvvatova Ziyoda was born on September 13, 2001 in Amudarya district of Karakalpakstan Republic. She is currently 3rd stage student of Foreign languages at Nukus Pedagogical Institute after named Ajiniyaz. She is keen on many specialities. She is very interested in poetry since childhood and she has beautiful goals for great success and her bright future. In 2018, her first poem "Tabrik" written for the New Year was published in "Mening oilam" newspaper of "Taraqqiyot Ko'zgusi" editorship in Amudarya district.

Recently, her poetry has been published in the Moldava anthology and is available for sale on "More Books" site and many other reputable sites.

So, she was delegate of the 3rd season of the "Talented Youth Forum" project, the owner of a forum ticket, a special certificate, a letter of recommendation and a letter of thanks in the name of parents and an active participant.

THE RAY OF THE SUN TOUCHES THE SHOULDER, OUR DAY WILL COME, OF COURSE, TOMORROW

We have set out in the light of knowledge,

May every heart shine with this light.

We are among the bookish youth,

May God protect us in this way.

Excellence in knowledge, strength in unity

You will tell me one day, of course, thank you!!!

We never stop looking,

Help is always our motto.

It's too late to get knowledge.

We burn like hearts.

Excellence in knowledge, strength in unity

You will tell me one day, of course, thank you!!!

Come, my friend, learn, burn, burn,

Let us not turn back from the path of knowledge.

May our Lord help us every moment,

Let everyone learn from our motto.

Excellence in knowledge, strength in unity

You will tell me one day, of course, thank you!!!

Our flight to the skies,

Our united team, always a moment.

Our great far-seeing peak,

Let's take a step without fear.

Excellence in knowledge, strength in unity

You will tell me one day, of course, thank you!!!

Our address is clear, our eyes of knowledge,

We go smoothly on this road without stumbling.

Let our word be an unforgettable slogan,

A great sign for the future generation.

Excellence in knowledge, strength in unity

You will tell me one day, of course, thank you!!!

About the project "Let's Rise Together".

HEAVEN UNDER THE FEET OF MOTHERS

Who truly loved us in this world,

She even gave everything to us.

She always filled what little we had,

Paradise under the feet of mothers!!!

If we fall, we seek refuge in God,

"Don't worry, baby!" prayed that

Was the only angel on earth,

Paradise under the feet of mothers!!!

MY GRANDMOTHER! (TO MY GRANDMOTHER)

My grandmother, whose kindness is equal to the world,

I can't say enough good things about you.

My prayer, my angel,

They think of us all the time.

Your hand is praying for our sustenance,

May God protect you.

Because of your prayers in the palms of your hands,

Our life is beautiful, you are our angel.

In our people: "Don't take gold, get blessing!", -

Elderly scholars used to say.

May God help us every moment,

We praise God.

Grandmother who spared no mercy,

 I always ask God for happiness.

God, you will be a hundred years old,

You will be the leader in our weddings.

Ikromova Ominakhan

Ikromova Ominakhan was born in Andijan in 2003.

Andijan State Pedagogical Institute, primary education student, 2nd stage.

"The best student" won the 1st place at the institute stage of the Republican competition and was awarded with a cash prize of 3 million soums.

He participated in the international contest organized among the CIS countries and was awarded the "Initiative reformer" Estonian badge with his scientific works.

According to the order of the Scientific Center of Advanced Research No. 03 dated January 13, 2023, he was awarded the Estonian badge "Pride of Science".

The goals and tasks of reading classes, educational and educational importance

Annotations: This article contains information about the educational and educational importance of reading classes for children and ways to provide them with the necessary knowledge and skills. Information is provided on how to improve children's thinking through reading lessons.

Key words: DTS, analytical, synthetic stages, fast reading, conscious reading, annotation.

Reading classes of primary classes have a special place in the education system according to their essence, goals and tasks. Because the foundations of literacy and moral-educational education are based on it. Therefore, the education of other subjects cannot be imagined without the education of reading. The student is faced with the ability to read the text correctly, quickly, understand it, and master its content for the first time in the reading classes. Through the reading classes, the way is opened for students to acquire knowledge and skills, which are expected to be mastered according to the requirements of the State Education Standard (DTS). It is in reading education that a person's desire to understand himself, and secondly, the world, is stimulated. For this purpose, the "Reading book" textbooks include various topics such as mother nature, the world around us, the history and current image of our country, the lives of adults and children, hard work, independence and national-spiritual values, friendship and peace among peoples. Artistic, moral-educational, scientific popular works designed to provide comprehensive understanding of "winter" is organized in the style of storytelling based on pictures, after mastering the reading technique, reading is carried out on the basis of artistic, scientific and popular texts selected on specific topics. Topics are determined by bringing students into the magical world of fiction, focusing on the correct formation of their worldviews based on the ideology of national independence. Accordingly, the main feature of the reading classes is to ensure students' literacy, and to educate them in the spirit of high moral values based on the national ideology. The subject range of the works studied in the reading lessons of primary grades is quite wide, and they are within the framework of general topics such as mother nature, seasons, folklore, love of work, major holiday dates, national independence and spirituality. Combined. The topics chosen for the reading lessons are intended to provide students with knowledge and education on everyday life, strengthening of independence and human relations. Among them, the themes of independence, homeland, spirituality and nature stand out. Their goal is self-awareness, to awaken feelings related to independence, homeland and nature. Topics such as patriotism, the world around us, hard work are comprehensive topics in textbooks, and are included in the section "My mother's golden cradle" in the 2nd grade "Reading book", "My Uzbekistan" {H. Imonberdiyev), "Istiqlal" (J.Jabborov), "Country" (E.Vahidov), "To the mountains" (U.Nasir), "Motherland" in the section "One mother, one country" in the 3rd grade poem about" (A. Avloni), , , Uzbegim" (E. Vahidov), "The homeland is respectable" (X. Davron), "Know that the homeland is waiting for you" (T. Malik) , in the 4th grade, "Tashkentnoma" (M. Shaykhzoda) is subjected to detailed analysis. Topics of socio-historical content give a certain idea about the past of our country, the life of our people, heroic struggle, works done by great figures, historical dates. Beruni, Amir About Temur, Alisher Navoi, Babur and other ancestors The texts are among them. This type of works not only introduces the students to our past, but also helps them to deeply understand their filial duty and responsibility towards the Motherland. This is how the feeling of love for the Motherland is formed in them. In the process of getting acquainted with the works that tell about the past of our country and analyzing them, the students will have the opportunity to compare the past with the present day, they will have a brief understanding of the development of the society. In this regard, H. Imonberdiyev's "My Uzbekistan", J. Jabbarov's "Istiqlol11(2nd class), A. Rustamov's "What is the flag?", A. Obidjon's "O'ktam" (3 -class), S. Barnoyev's works on the topic "Mangulikka tatigulik kun", E. Malikov's "Hello, Neksiya!" (4th class) will help closely. With the help of topics related to nature, students acquire knowledge about changes in nature, the change of seasons, and the animal world. Works on this topic teach students to be observant, to love nature, to have the right attitude towards it. When working on texts about nature images, a trip to the bosom of nature is organized and children are taught to be observant, if the analysis of works on patriotism is carried out by means of meetings with famous people of the country or showing films related to the topic, the effectiveness of the lesson will increase. In general, all topics in the "Reading Book" textbooks are aimed at educating students, enriching their vocabulary, forming their oral and written speech correctly, and developing speech culture. In the current "Reading Book" textbooks, it is taken into account that the materials expand from class to class both in terms of subject and content. For example, the topics taught in the 1st grade, such as "Our ancestors are our pride", "Pt ~ the light of the mind", "Emerald spring", "Silver winter" were continued in the 2nd-4th grades. Fills and enriches. In contrast to other stages of continuous education, the formation of students' reading skills, working on the text of the work is the didactic goal of education in the reading classes of primary grades. It is based on texts on various topics through work, it is closely connected with spiritual-ethical, literary-aesthetic education. Particular attention is paid to the variety of genres, poetic perfection of the texts selected for each topic in the textbooks, and their compatibility with the students' level of knowledge and age characteristics. It is one of the important tasks for teachers to make students understand that the knowledge, skills, and abilities acquired with the help of textbooks will be necessary in the future life. Implementation of the requirements for reading education in the DTS and "Mother Tongue" curriculum, proper organization of classroom learning, teaching stages, principles and methods, first of all , largely depends on the appropriate use of advanced pedagogical technologies. In general, the didactic tasks set for reading classes are as follows: 1. Formation of good reading qualities in students: correct, fast, conscious, expressive reading. 2. To teach students to use the book, to get the necessary knowledge from it, to instill a love for the book; to raise them from a simple reader to a thoughtful, creative reader. 3. Expanding and enriching students' knowledge about the environment and forming their scientific outlook. 4. Educate students in the spirit of moral, aesthetic maturity and love for work. 5.

Cultivating students' connected speech and literary-aesthetic thinking. 6. Enriching the imagination of students. 7. Formation of elementary literary ideas. It should not be forgotten that there are clear and scientific methodical methods of performing each educational task, which are being enriched with modern teaching methods. These tasks are solved in relation to others and in the course of study activities outside the classroom.

Reading skills and ways to improve them

Reading skills mean reading the text of an artistic work correctly, quickly, consciously and expressively. Students' reading skills are formed and improved in reading lessons. The qualities of reading skills are interrelated, and their basis is conscious reading. If the reader reads the text quickly and correctly, but does not read with understanding, or as a result of his fast reading, others do not understand the content of the text, if he reads correctly, then he reads very slowly. In short, if one does not pay attention to the pauses between speech units, the thought expressed in the text will not be understood. Reading at a certain speed and accuracy is the basis of conscious reading, and accurate, fast and conscious reading is the basis of expressive reading. The analytical stage corresponds to the period of literacy training, in which the ability to analyze words by syllables and letters and to read in syllables is formed. For the synthetic stage, the reading of the word is characteristic; in this case, the perception of the word by sight and its pronunciation are mainly consistent with the understanding of the meaning of the word. Reading is done by understanding the meaning of words. Students move to the synthetic stage in the 3rd grade. In the following years, learning will be automated. Work on the work in reading lessons should be organized in such a way that the analysis of the content of the work is aimed at improving reading skills. Correct reading. Correct reading means reading without making mistakes, that is, correct reading is without breaking the sound-letter composition of the word, grammatical forms, the sound or syllable in the word It is reading without omitting inni, without adding another sound, without changing the place of letters, pronouncing it clearly and putting the accent on the word correctly. M.Odilova and T.Ashrapova state that "all the requirements for the standards of literary pronunciation also apply to the ability to read correctly." Defined as follows: "Correct reading is the accurate and uniform copying of the material by sound." Therefore, correct reading is reading based on literary and orthoepic standards without violating the sound structure and grammatical form of the word. Because elementary students lack a thorough synthesis between comprehension, pronunciation, and understanding of text content, they make reading errors. This makes it difficult to understand the content of the text. Correct reading depends on the length and brevity of the word, the reader's vocabulary, that is, how much he knows the lexical meaning of the word, and the syllabic and morphemic composition of the word. . Students often make mistakes for the following reasons:

1. Since there is a careful synthesis between pronouncing a word and understanding its meaning, the child sees the sound side of the word first, and is in a hurry to pronounce it. He ignores the meaning of the word.

2. The word is polysyllabic, and the child makes a mistake if he has not heard it before.

3. Makes a mistake due to not knowing the meaning of the word.

4. Makes the mistake of reading quickly.

5. Correct reading also depends on the light and how the light falls.

6. They have difficulty reading words with closed syllables in the middle and at the end of a consonant. Fast reading. Fast reading is reading at a normal speed, in which the speed of reading should not be separated from the understanding of the content of the text. The speed of reading should increase in accordance with the speed of understanding the text. Reading that provides mastery of the content of the read work, conscious perception of the content of the text is called fast reading. Reading speed is defined as the number of words read per minute. In the reading program announced in 2005, the speed of reading in the second semester of the 1st grade is 20-25 words (the speed of reading an unfamiliar text is also 20-25

words); 25-30 words at the end of the school year; In the first semester of the 2nd grade, the speed of reading the text is 30-35 words; 40-50 words in the 2nd semester; 60-70 words in the 1st semester of the 3rd grade; 70-80 words in the 2nd semester; In the 1st half of the 4th grade, 110-130 words without voice, 90-100 words in voice reading are defined.

Experiments show that if a child reads a text with 250 words in one minute, he remembers 200 words in it. If he reads by letters and syllables, his focus will be on syllables, not words. As a result, he cannot remember words. Applying this to the reading speed of a 4th grader will remember 100 out of 125 words. This allows to achieve high performance. In the 4th grade, there are students who read 170-180 words per minute. Mindful reading. Mindful reading is a key quality of good reading. Conscious reading is reading with understanding the exact content of the read text, the ideological direction of the work, images and the role of artistic means, as well as being able to express one's attitude to the events described in the work. Conscious reading, in turn, depends on the students' necessary life experience, understanding of the lexical meaning of the word, the connection of words in the sentence, and a number of methodological conditions. Currently, the term conscious reading is used in the literature and school experience in two senses: firstly, in the sense of a reading technique in relation to mastering the reading process, and secondly, in the sense of one of the qualities of reading in relation to reading in a broad sense. Will be done. Intonation (tone). Intonation is the sum of the elements of oral speech acting together: emphasis, tempo and rhythm of speech, pauses, and the volume of the voice. These three types of schooling alternate. In the 1st-2nd grades, it is switched from reading aloud and whispering (whispering) to internal reading, and in the 3rd-4th grades, it is switched from internal reading to aloud reading. There is no limit on the use of study types in 3-4 grades. In elementary grades, the same requirement is imposed on all types of reading, that is, it is necessary to read correctly, quickly, consciously and expressively.

CONCLUSION. Today, a number of large-scale activities are being carried out in order to further strengthen the interest of young people in books, at the same time, it should be noted that every year in Uzbekistan, young people spend their free time meaningfully and awaken their love for books. Various contests are being held throughout the Republic, one of them is the "Young Reader" contest. Through this competition, a number of young people read more than 50, 60 books and win Spark and a number of valuable gifts. As the President of the Republic of Uzbekistan, Shavkat Mirziyoyev, said, "Win a book and make your parents happy", which means that the more books we read, the more our knowledge, world view and imagination will expand.

REFERENCES:

1. A. Zunnunov et al. Literature teaching methodology. — T.: "Teacher 41, 1992.

2. A. Rafiyev. Uzbek alphabet and spelling based on Latin script. — T.: 2003.

3. A. Ghulamov. Principles and methods of mother tongue teaching. – T.: "Teacher", 1992.

4. B. Ma'qulova, T. Adashboyev. My book is my sun (a book for extracurricular reading for 1st grade). — T.: "Teacher", 1999.

5. B. Ma'qulova, S. Sa'diyeva. Extracurricular reading activities (methodical guide for 1st grade teachers). — T.: "Teacher", 1997.

6. B. Ma'kulova, S. Matchon. Kitabim-aftobim (a book for extracurricular reading for 2nd grade). — T.: "Teacher", 2000.

7. V. Ma'qulova, D. Nasriddinova. My book is my sun (reading book beyond the 1st grade). — T.: "Teacher" NMIU, 2008.

8. Criteria for creating primary school textbooks / Compilers: Q. Abdullayeva, M. Ochilov, K. Nazarov, S. Fuzailov, N. Bikboyeva. — T.: 1994.

9. J.G. Yoldoshev, S. A. Usmanov. Fundamentals of pedagogical technology. — T.: "Teacher", 2004.

10. Y. Abdullayev. Teaching literacy in the old school. – T.: "Teacher", 1960.

11. K. Kasimova. Teaching difficult spelling words in elementary grades. — T.: 1964.

12. K. Kasimova, S. Fuzailov, A. Nematova. Mother tongue (textbook for grade 2). — T.: Cholpon, 2005. 13. K. Kasimova, A. Nematova. Mother tongue lessons in the 2nd grade. — T.: Cholpon, 2004.

Ashirova Oghiloy

Ashirova Oghiloy 2nd stage master's student of Gulistan State University, designer of Vocational School No. 2 of Sayhunabad District.

The responsibility of parents in the development of children's mental activity, the role of early education methods and books at home

Annotations: Today, parents pay a lot of attention to the question of what to teach their child after the age of three. However, according to modern research, 70-80 percent of brain cells have developed by this age. Therefore, it is necessary for parents to have knowledge about what they should pay attention to in the education and upbringing of their child under the age of three. We can call the education of children up to three years old as "early education".

Key words: Early education, child success, book, library, vocabulary, research.

The most important task for a mother is raising a child. Today's modern mothers need to develop their own personal approach rather than using outdated, old-fashioned parenting methods. If a mother is not only an educator, but also a doctor, designer, nutritionist, spiritual coach, pedagogue, psychologist, it will be useful for her child's future.

The child's brain should be given various information that stimulates its development and reveals its abilities as soon as possible. According to many psychologists and specialists in brain physiology, useful information coming to the brain from infancy opens up the child's abilities and develops independence in him.

The period from birth to three years of age is the period when intercellular connections are most actively formed. A person's abilities and character are almost formed in the period from birth to three years. That's why it seems unfair that a gifted child goes to school without any difficulty, and an underdeveloped child always spends a long time and has to acquire knowledge with difficulty, but this is a situation that can never be lost. . It all depends on the life stage that decides the child's future, that is, the level of development of the baby's brain before the age of three. That's why the period from birth to three years and the education given up to this age is very important.

Modern pedagogues and psychologists emphasize that parents are equally responsible for a child's education and upbringing, and that both have their roles and responsibilities. The Japanese Masaru Ibuka, who created a new theory about the development of children during infancy, and is known to the world, expressed the following thoughts about this: "Neural connections are quickly formed in the brain of a baby before the age of three. During this period, I would like mothers to be ready not to give their child's contact to anyone. It is necessary for fathers to help mothers in carrying out such important tasks of raising a child, to support the mother with all their strength, both spiritually and materially." Based on my five years of observation and life experiences, there are many ways that a child who receives proper upbringing and attention under the constant supervision of his mother until the age of three can grow up to be well-educated, talented and energetic. Observed, that is, no one can understand a child like his mother.

What does the child's success depend on?

Researchers at the University of California were interested in finding an answer to this question. They have developed the most comprehensive scientific research on this topic. The research lasted 20 years. The number of participating countries is 27, and the number of participants is more than 70,000. The results were published in 2010.

The answer to the question is a lot of books at home! Children of families with a lot of books at home get more education and earn more. A good library brings intelligence and money!

The most exciting result of the giant study is this: it turns out that the number of books in the house is more important than the country you were born in, the level of education of your family, the prosperity of the country, your profession and the political system of the country! This is indeed very good news. Because reading a book is an affordable and affordable tool. A good library also means equal opportunities. Every parent who wants to leave the world without dreams leaves a good library for their children.

The difference between a house without books and a house with more than 500 books is as big as the difference between parents who are uneducated, have low education (school) or higher education (15-16 years of education). Those whose parents have a higher education have an average of 3.2 years of education. If you don't have a college degree, don't worry. Being in a house with at least 500 books gives the same result. Only the content is important, not the number of books! By purchasing these books, you are a person who believes in the power of useful knowledge, is conscious of success, and cares about your child's success. Now you know what is the greatest legacy you can leave to your child. In our time, power comes from knowledge, and a book is a storehouse of knowledge. Books are an equal opportunity tool.

The last material legacy you leave to your children is your property. Medium Legacy is your library. The first legacy is your vocabulary.

The first legacy you leave to your children is your vocabulary. What they learn from you is their initial investment in life. Have you ever thought about how many words you used when talking to your child until he was 3 years old? Can you guess how much the words you say to him as a baby will affect his success in school?

Betty Hart and Todd Risley of the University of Kansas conducted extensive research in the field of education in the 1960s. They designed a study involving 42 families. They got to know the families and followed the children from 7 months to 3 years old in the houses.

The results are interesting:

• 86 to 98 percent of the words a child uses before the age of three come from their parents' language base.

• The child not only uses the words used in the family, but also the number of words he uses, the length of his conversation and speech are very similar to his parents.

It has been proven that the foundation formed before the age of three has a strong influence on the success of the school in the following years. There is a significant correlation between achievement at age 3 and achievement at age 9 and 10 on tests measuring language and reading comprehension skills.

We are not only dependent on the people around us. Fortunately, there are books in the world! That's why books exist! According to research, reading to children increases their vocabulary more than talking to them.

Another aspect that is as important as the number of words used is the amount of praise and criticism in the content of the conversation. A well-known and supportive language "tig" has a great influence on the success of children. It was also studied whether the words used in the family are positive or negative.

According to the research results:

• In respectable families, 1 negative word corresponds to 6 positive words.

• For children of low-income families, this indicator corresponds to 2 positive words and 1 negative word. This indicator indicates a high level of "tongue injury".

In the psychology of language, to achieve 1 wrong 5 right, it is advisable not to use wrong words at all, it is better not to make a mistake than to try to compensate for it. Increasing vocabulary and avoiding language injuries should be the main goal of development.

The "starting investment" of social success that we provide to children is our words. First, they receive our words, then they understand the lessons in school through these words, this understanding gives them confidence, and the increased confidence makes them more eager to learn. 'ladi, then they will be successful in their life. Because they will learn from it. The deeper, richer and wider the vocabulary that makes up their inner world, the more they can dominate the outer world.

In conclusion, we should pay attention to the child's brain before the age of three, when it has rare abilities. If the mother chooses only primitive picture books for the child, the neural system of the child's brain will be formed in such a way that this system will not be able to accept anything other than such simple pictures. Because of this, he will face difficulties when he grows up. Whether you understand it or not, you should definitely try. A small baby's brain absorbs everything it can take in. In this way, his mind develops. Many scientists agree with this opinion.

When a child hears words and sees them written at the same time, the sounds are filled with written symbols, and the symbols with sounds, thus they reinforce each other and are better remembered. Nevertheless, adults express the opinion that it is too early to teach letters to a baby who has just started talking, and it is too difficult for the child. When the baby learns new words, it is necessary to show him how the words are written as much as possible. He remembers words correctly as they are written and does not confuse them with other words.

References:

1. Masaru Ibuka "Evening after three" Tashkent. "Academic Edition" 2021.

2. Masaru Ibuka "It's Time Until Three" Tashkent. "Academic Edition" 2021.

3. Momin Sekman Dr. Spring Melting. "How children achieve success" Tashkent. "Generation of the New Century" 2022.

4. O'.A. Ashirova "The importance of early education in the mental development of children" Journal of New Century Innovations.2022

5. O'.A. Ashirova, S.A. Mavlonova "The role of early education, Fine Mechanics and mental arithmetic and raising the intelligence activity of children and developing their independence". Science and educations in XXI century. 2022.

6. O'.A. Ashirova, S.A. Mavlonova. "The importance of breastfeeding in children of early age". International Conference by name "International Conference on Learning and Teaching.2022/1.

7. O'.A. Ashirova. "Basics of early education in the child's mental development". European Multidisciplinary Journal of Modern Science. 2022.

Esonova Shahzoda

Esonova Shahzoda was born on June 6, 2006 in Kitab district, Kashkadarya region. He is currently studying in the 10th grade of school 39 in Samarkand.

Because of his interest in literature, he swings his pen in the direction of poetry. To date, 2 poetry collections of the artist have been published.

2020 is the year of the Motherland.

2022 is the Anthem of Life.

In addition, the artist's poems were published in regional and republican newspapers.

YOU ARE MY COUNTRY

Nightingales fly in gardens,

They live in seven climates.

Poets sing poems to the nightingale,

This is my homeland, my homeland.

Jambil basil in the miracle garden,

In a huge mountain full of herbs.

The beauty is in the spot of the moon,

This is my homeland, my homeland.

Temur the Great rocked his cradle,

God told my grandfather Navoi.

Babur missed Mirza and waited,

This is my homeland, my homeland.

The ancestral line is far away,

This is forever in history.

Today, we young people understand,

This is my homeland, my homeland.

This is the land drawn by Kamoliddin Behzod.

This is the land where Ulugbek Samo traveled.

It is an indescribable land.

This is my homeland, my homeland!

SAMARKAND

Samarkand roy has polished the ground,

You will never lose your cool.

In the bosom where great breeds grew

The fairies are in the land of broken dice.

The garden is full of yellow fruits,

Always open arms to guests.

 Mother is the only land on earth,

There are many delicacies on the table.

The grain ripens in the sun,

Delicious bread that is not baked in a foreign country.

 Even Babur missed the smell of bread,

He left the world with homesickness.

Silver market, famous in Europe,

Figs are a cure for a thousand and one ailments.

Their mothers are beautiful, their daughters are beautiful,

The guys are funny and brave.

Ulugbek conquered the sky,

This is forever in history.

Temur occupied the earth,

He left Samarkand a legacy.

My dear country, Uzbekistan,

If Tashkent is the head, Registan is the heart.

Gives the city a unique expression,

Ulugbek, Tillakori and Sherdar.

OUR FOOTBALL STAR

Received education at Mash'al Academy,

He goes to the field to say victory.

Show yourself in the ranks of the team,

Every word he says with a goal.

He shone in Rostov's ranks,

He called the team to victory.

Wherever he is, he is always a winner.

Here is Eldor, who will titrate the A series.

I wish you luck in Italy,

Win, score only.

Always keep moving forward.

Don't forget Eldar only win!

Hamidullayeva Ziynatkhon... 3

Sherova Orzigul 7

Khoshimova Shahinabonu.. 11

Ikromova Ominakhan 20

Ashirova Oghiloy 32

Esonova Shahzoda.. 40

Printed by Books on Demand GmbH, Norderstedt / Germany